Year 2

Test C, Paper 2
Reading Booklet

Contents

Oleg the Giant · · · · · · · · · · · · 3

Oscar's Zoo · · · · · · · · · · · · 6

Acknowledgements
The publisher gratefully acknowledges permission to reproduce the following copyright material:

Graham Fletcher for the use of 'Oleg the Giant'. Text © 2015, Graham Fletcher.
Graham Fletcher for the use of 'Oscar's Zoo'. Text © 2015, Graham Fletcher.

Illustrations for Reading Booklet C:
With thanks to Les Scholes for permission to reproduce his illustrations for Oleg the Giant and Oscar's Zoo © 2015.

OLEG THE GIANT

At four feet eleven inches, Oleg was a giant. Four feet eleven inches may not be very tall in your world, but it was in Oleg's. He was not the biggest giant in his world, but he would be when he was fully grown.

Oleg lived next to his village. All the giants in Oleg's world had a village and this one was his. Oleg had lived there all his life, but something was not quite right about it.

When he was very young, Oleg had played with the village children, but as he had grown, he had become too big for them. He didn't fit into the park any more. He didn't fit into his house. He didn't fit into his clothes.

In fact, Oleg just didn't fit in at all.

When the village children didn't call for him to play any more, Oleg just sat alone outside the village and cried.

You might know someone like Oleg. You might be like Oleg. You might understand him. If you did, you could explain to him that it's all right not to fit in. Oleg might not understand though, because Oleg didn't understand himself.

The villagers did not like it when Oleg cried. The tears dripped down his nose and onto the ground, forming huge lakes. The rivers overflowed and flooded the streets. Some of the houses were swept away with the tide, sometimes with their owners still in them.

Oleg did not want to cause the villagers any harm. After all, he was their giant and they were his villagers, so he asked his mother what to do. She gave him a blanket to dry his eyes. This worked well until it got soaked. Oleg squeezed the blanket to wring it out, but the villagers complained that it was like a thunderstorm. That just made Oleg cry some more.

So Oleg sat on the hill outside the village by himself. Sometimes he cried and the villagers moaned. Sometimes he sighed and the villagers groaned.

The Lord Mayor knew that he had to talk to Oleg. The people in the next village were complaining now. This had all gone far enough, and he had to put a stop to it.

Oleg had cried so much that the entire area around the hill was a lake. He would have been up to his ankles in water if he had not sat on top of the hill.

Ankle deep may not be very deep in your world, but it was in Oleg's.

The Lord Mayor called for the navy to take him to Oleg. Unfortunately, the village was miles from the sea, so it didn't have a navy.

Was the Lord Mayor bothered by the lack of a navy? No, not a bit. He just invented one and made himself the High Sea Lord.

The Lord Mayor rowed across the lake. It was so new it didn't have a name, so the Lord Mayor named it after himself. So, the Lord Mayor rowed across Lord Mayor Lake to see Oleg.

"The villagers are ashamed of you," said the Lord Mayor.

Oleg was ashamed of himself. He sobbed and the Lord Mayor put up an umbrella to avoid being drenched. He was not going to give up. A little bit of water wasn't going to stop him!

He peeped out from under the umbrella and was caught full in the face by a teardrop that knocked him over and sank the boat.

SCHOLASTIC Reading Booklet

The Lord Mayor wasn't the Lord Mayor for nothing. He was good at everything. He swam to the upturned umbrella and climbed into that.

"The people are fed up with you," he said. "All the other villages have real giants. We are a laughing stock. Why can't you be a real giant and do what real giants do?"

Oleg was ashamed. He wanted to be a real giant.

"We want a proper giant like all the other villages have."

Oleg was more ashamed. He didn't know what proper giants did. He was only a little giant.

"Proper giants *RAAAH* a lot and terrify their villagers. Proper giants are horrible and fearsome. Proper giants eat cows and rip up trees."

Oleg hadn't got any *RAAAH* in him. He didn't want to be horrible and fearsome. He didn't fancy eating cows. He liked beans more.

"You're our giant. Either be the giant we want or go somewhere else!"

Oleg was even more ashamed. They were his villagers and he was their giant, but he couldn't be the giant they wanted. It just wasn't in him, so he pulled himself up to his pathetic four feet eleven inches, turned sadly and sloshed away through the ankle-deep water, sinking the Lord Mayor's umbrella in a tidal wave behind him.

So Oleg left his problems behind him, but you know that's not the end, don't you? Sometimes what we think we want isn't what we really want at all. But you knew that, didn't you? If you knew Oleg, you might have told him.

Oscar's Zoo

Some zoos are large, some zoos are small,
but Oscar's Zoo takes up no space at all.
Tucked up each night in his jungle bed,
his zoo fills the dreams inside Oscar's head.

What strange animals can be found in its grounds?
What marvellous beasts, what wonderful sounds?

An Alliphant and an Elegator
Squashed into the elevator.
A Wallabear and Koalaby
Perched together in a tree.

There are ants in pants and some in skirts,
Goats in coats on top of their shirts,
Crocs in socks, a bat in a hat,
Gnus in shoes, well fancy all that!

Every night is an animals' feast
and all are included from greatest to least.
They mingle, they mutter, they squeak and
they squawk.
They jingle, they flutter and some even talk!

As he slumbers each night, clutching his teddy,
Oscar's Zoo is open, waiting and ready.
But every dawn, as night turns to day,
the zoo closes its gates and then fades away.

As Oscar wakes up, stretching and yawning,
his zoo disappears and is gone in the morning.
Oscar's Zoo is a secret, of which nothing is said,
known only to Oscar, to me, you and Ted.

Graham Fletcher (2015)

[BLANK PAGE]

[BLANK PAGE]

Guidance and mark schemes for Reading: Year 2

Contents	Page
About this pack	4
Advice for parents and carers	5
Advice for children	6
Test coverage	7
Marking and assessing the papers	7
Marks table	7
Test A	
Paper 1: Mark scheme	8
Paper 2: Mark scheme	9
Test B	
Paper 1: Mark scheme	10
Paper 2: Mark scheme	12
Test C	
Paper 1: Mark scheme	13
Paper 2: Mark scheme	14

About this pack

This pack provides you with practice papers to help support children with the Key Stage 1 Reading test. The pack consists of this introductory booklet (including mark schemes) and three sample tests covering a wide range of content taken from the Key Stage 1 programme of study.

Using the practice papers

The practice papers in this pack can be used as you would any other practice materials. The children will need to be familiar with specific test-focused skills, such as reading carefully, leaving questions until the end if they seem too difficult, working at a suitable pace and checking through their work.

About the tests

Each Reading test has two papers:

- Paper 1: the reading text is mixed with questions in a single booklet. Children have about 30 minutes to read the text and answer the questions.

- Paper 2: there is a reading booklet containing a range of texts and a separate question booklet. Children have about 40 minutes to read all the texts and answer the questions. Children should refer back to the reading booklet for their answers.

Neither paper should be strictly timed. You should ensure that every child has enough time to demonstrate what he or she understands, knows and can do, without prolonging the test inappropriately. Use your judgement to decide when, or if, children need breaks during the assessment, and whether to stop the test early if appropriate.

The marks available for each question are shown in the answer booklet next to each question and are also shown next to each answer in the mark scheme. Incorrect answers do not get a mark and no half marks should be given.

There are three different types of answer.

- **Selected answers:** children may be required to choose an option from a list, draw lines to match answers, or tick a correct answer. Usually 1 mark will be awarded.

- **Short answers:** children will need to write a phrase from the text or use information from it. Usually 1 mark will be awarded.

- **Several line answers:** children will need to write a sentence or two. Usually 1–2 marks will be awarded.

- **Longer answers:** children will usually need to write more than one sentence using information from the text. Up to 2 marks will be awarded.

For Paper 1, a selection of 'useful words' are also provided on page 3. Discuss these words with your child before they start the test and make sure they understand them.

Advice for parents and carers

How this pack will help

This pack will support your child to get ready for the KS1 National Reading Tests. It provides valuable practice and help on the responses and content expected of Year 2 children aged 6–7 years.

In the weeks leading up to the National Tests, your child may be given plenty of practice, revision and tips to give them the best possible chance to demonstrate their knowledge and understanding. It is helpful to try to practise outside of school and many children benefit from extra input. This pack will help your child prepare and build their confidence.

In this pack you will find three Reading tests. The layout and format of each test closely matches those used in the National Tests, so your child will become familiar with what to expect and get used to the style of the tests. In this booklet you will find a comprehensive answer section and guidance about how to mark the questions.

Tips

- Make sure that you allow your child to take the test in a quiet environment where they are not likely to be interrupted or distracted.

- Make sure your child has a flat surface to work on, with plenty of space to spread out and good light.

- Emphasise the importance of reading and re-reading a question.

- These tests are similar to the ones your child will take in May in Year 2 and they therefore give you a good idea of strengths and areas for development. When you have found areas that require some more practice, it is useful to go over these again and practise similar types of question with your child.

- Go through the tests again together, identify any gaps in learning and address any misconceptions or areas of misunderstanding. If you are unsure of anything yourself, then make an appointment to see your child's teacher who will be able to help and advise further.

- Practising little and often will enable your child to build up confidence and skills over a period of time.

Advice for children

What to do before the test

- Revise and practise regularly.
- Spend some time each week practising.
- Focus on the areas you are less sure of to get better.
- Get a good night's sleep and eat a healthy breakfast.
- Be on time for school.
- Make sure you have all the things you need.

Test coverage

Children will need to be able to:

- Use their knowledge of vocabulary to understand texts.
- Identify and explain key aspects of fiction and non-fiction including characters, titles, events and information.
- Identify and explain the sequence of events in texts.
- Make inferences from the text.
- Predict what might happen.

Marking and assessing the papers

The mark schemes and answers are located next in this booklet.

The mark schemes provide detailed examples of correct answers (although other variations/phrasings are often acceptable) and an explanation about what the answer should contain to be awarded a mark or marks.

Although the mark scheme sometimes contains alternative suggestions for correct answers, some children may find other ways of expressing a correct answer. When marking these tests, exercise judgement when assessing the accuracy or relevance of an answer and give credit for correct responses.

Marks table

At the back of each booklet there is a table for you to insert the number of marks achieved for each question. This will enable you to see which areas your child needs to practise further.

National Standard in Reading

The mark that your child gets in the test paper will be known as the 'raw score' (for example, '22' in 22/40). The raw score will be converted to a scaled score and children achieving a scaled score of 100 or more will achieve the National Standard in that subject. These 'scaled scores' enable results to be reported consistently year-on-year.

The guidance in the table below shows the marks that children need to achieve to reach the National Standard. This should be treated as a guide only, as the number of marks may vary. You can also find up-to-date information about scaled scores on our website: www.scholastic.co.uk/nationaltests

Marks achieved	Standard
0–21	Has not met the National Standard in Reading for Key Stage 1
22–40	Has met the National Standard in Reading for Key Stage 1

Mark scheme for Test A: Paper 1

Q	Answers	Marks
	Practice question: months	
1	**Award 1 mark** for any one of the following: • Backseat waited and waited. • He was a very patient dog. • He waited for days, he waited for months. Or a summary, such as: *Backseat waited a long time for his Special Day.*	1
2	**Award 1 mark** for his Special Day	1
3	**Award 1 mark** for all three answers correct: You are given presents. You play special games. You have a special cake.	1
4	**Award 1 mark** for both answers correct: • He lay in all the wrong places. • He sat in the back seat of the car.	1
5	**Award 1 mark** for he was told to go away.	1
6	**Award 1 mark** for all three answers correct: reading, talking, stroking cats	1
7	**Award 1 mark** for: to be a useful dog	1
8	**Award 1 mark** for snuffled	1
9	**Award 1 mark** for either of the following: No one noticed that *he* had found the pencil case. Or: They thought it had been in the bag all the time!	1
10	**Award 1 mark** for all three correct: Backseat was very helpful. 4 Backseat sat in the back of the car. 2 Backseat wanted a Special Day. 1 The family told Backseat to go away. 3	1
11	**Award 1 mark** for: The Sad Dog	1
12	**Award 1 mark** for any plausible answer that includes a reason, such as: Yes, because Backseat will keep on finding ways to remind the family. No, because the family will continue to ignore him.	1
13	**Award 1 mark** for the number is the same or similar.	1
14	**Award 1 mark** for It is a lot to write by hand or You can print them out or similar.	1
15	**Award 1 mark** for all three answers correct: the person's name; where the party will be; what time the party starts	1
16	**Award 1 mark** for each of the following, in either order: 1. what the invitation is for 2. what time it ends	2
17	**Award 1 mark** for so people know who has sent it or similar.	1
18	**Award 1 mark** for: 5 o'clock	1
19	**Award 1 mark** for: signature	1

■SCHOLASTIC Guidance and mark schemes

Mark scheme for Test A: Paper 2

Q	Answers	Marks
1	**Award 1 mark** for: unusual	1
2	**Award 1 mark** for on hilly ground/in hilly areas	1
3	**Award 1 mark** for 1pm	1
4	**Award 1 mark** for both answers correct. Happy Valley Farm Visitor Centre → You will see lots of animals. Happy Valley Farm Visitor Centre → You can touch the animals.	1
5	**Award 1 mark** for solve your problems, or similar.	1
6	**Award 1 mark** for: give up hope	1
7	**Award 1 mark** for: It is cheap and quick to make.	1
8	**Award 1 mark** for: To add stripes to your top	1
9	**Award 1 mark** for You will have a really good pirate costume, or similar.	1
10	**Award 1 mark** for (in) the park	1
11	**Award 1 mark** for: On a Sunday	1
12	**Award 1 mark** for: Wash the car	1
13	**Award 1 mark** for: With goals of jumpers in the park	1
14	**Award 1 mark** for each plausible reason based on the text, up to a maximum of **2 marks**, such as: • They play football. • He remembers what it was like to be young. • He gets to tell stories of when he was young.	2
15	**Award 1 mark** for all numbers correct. Then sitting round the kitchen table **4** I tried to win the FA Cup **1** On Sundays I rise, early morn **2** We play football till the dark **3**	1
16	**Award 1 mark** for all pairs of rhyming words correctly matched. same – game plan – gran up – cup park – dark	1
17	**Award 1 mark** for each plausible explanation, up to a maximum of **2 marks**, such as: • It is about the grandfather when he was a little boy and his grandson who is a little boy. • It is about the things that little boys do. • It is a good summary of the poem.	2
18	**Award 1 mark** for: Then and Now	1

Mark scheme for Test B: Paper 1

Q	Answers	Marks
	Practice question: a sheepdog	
1	**Award 1 mark** for Just before teatime **Do not accept**: before teatime or teatime.	1
2	**Award 1 mark** for: Mum	1
3	**Award 1 mark** for he might not get them all in safely, or similar.	1
4	**Award 1 mark** for: clouds gathering	1
5	**Award 1 mark** for he was worried about where Bess was, or similar.	1
6	**Award 1 mark** for (The wind could) blow down the old elm (onto the power lines).	1
7	**Award 1 mark** for all numbers correct. Sam can't see Bess. ⃝2 Dad's voice is lost in the wind. ⃝4 Dad is worried about the wind. ⃝1 The sheep are safe inside. ⃝3	1
8	**Award 1 mark** for He looked half frozen, He was very cold, or similar.	1
9	**Award 1 mark** for both lines drawn correctly to: • She is useless. • Being shut out will teach her a lesson.	1
10	**Award 1 mark** for: There is a storm outside but it is warm inside, or similar.	1
11	**Award 1 mark** for each of the following, up to a maximum of **2 marks**: • Bess will need a good hot bath when she gets in. • Will Bess be blown away? • I hope Bess doesn't have to dig her way home.	2
12	**Award 1 mark** for: The snow was blinding.	1
13	**Award 1 mark** for any plausible explanation for Bess's return; for example: • She could use her sense of smell to find her way back. • The weather might improve. • The story doesn't say she is hurt. • It would give the story a happy ending. • Sam is going to wait up until she comes home. • Bess loves Sam.	1
14	**Award 1 mark** for: The Lost Dog	1
15	**Award 1 mark** for: Water went over the top.	1
16	**Award 1 mark** for all three lines drawn correctly to: • It causes a lot of damage. • It destroys homes. • It makes people find other places to work.	1

Q	Answers	Marks
17	**Award 1 mark** for any clear explanation, such as: ● It tells people the weather will be bad. ● It tells people rain is coming. ● It tells people that floods might happen.	1
18	**Award 1 mark** for: Around rivers	1
19	**Award 1 mark** for any plausible suggestion of what might happen, such as: ● Rivers will continue to flood. ● Damage will continue to happen. ● People and buildings will not be safe.	1

Mark scheme for Test B: Paper 2

Q	Answers	Marks
1	**Award 1 mark** for: Our weather is quite good.	1
2	**Award 1 mark** for: They would melt.	1
3	**Award 1 mark** for They are very high.	1
4	**Award 1 mark** for Arizona (in America) **Do not accept**: (in) America.	1
5	**Award 1 mark** for: Clear skies	1
6	**Award 1 mark** for both lines drawn correctly to: • Not enough water • Too much water	1
7	**Award 2 marks** for: A time when there is very heavy rainfall for months, or similar. **Award 1 mark** for: Answers that only refer to heavy rain but do not include the amount of time.	2
8	**Award 1 mark** for any answer that refers to the strength or violence of the wind and rain.	1
9	**Award 1 mark** for: It is a giant wave.	1
10	**Award 1 mark** for keep the temperature up, or similar.	1
11	**Award 1 mark** for both lines drawn correctly to: • Summers are getting wetter. • Winters are getting less cold.	1
12	**Award 1 mark** for: The Earth freezes.	1
13	**Award 1 mark** for any answer that gives a reason for future climate change, such as: • It will continue to get warmer and wetter because that seems to be the way it is going. • It will get colder because we have not had an ice age for a long time. • Do not accept any answer that describes future climate change without giving a reason.	1
14	**Award 1 mark** for any answer that explains why the title is suitable, such as: • It tells you what the text is all about. • It is a summary of the text.	1
15	**Award 1 mark** for icy or chilly	1
16	**Award 1 mark** for a clap of thunder	1
17	**Award 1 mark** for: Splattering	1
18	**Award 1 mark** for all four words correct: night, bright, white, sight	1

SCHOLASTIC Guidance and mark schemes

Q	Answers	Marks
19	**Award 1 mark** for all numbers correct. a flash of lightning 4 a falling raindrop 2 a winter snowball 3 a ray of sunshine 1	1

Mark scheme for Test C: Paper 1

Q	Answers	Marks
	Practice question: Norway has a very long coast. One side of Norway borders the sea.	
1	**Award 1 mark** for: a country	1
2	**Award 1 mark** for: Norwegians	1
3	**Award 1 mark** for: York	1
4	**Award 1 mark** for: Jorvik Viking Centre	1
5	**Award 1 mark** for: a long way north	1
6	**Award 1 mark** for: There are very few daylight hours.	1
7	**Award 1 mark** for both answers correct: ● Whales ● Basking sharks	1
8	**Award 1 mark** for: there were no sharks / brown bears / polar bears / dangerous animals, or similar.	1
9	**Award 1 mark** for: its fjords	1
10	**Award 1 mark** for all three answers correct: ● They are long, narrow inlets from the sea. ● They have steep sides. ● They were made by glaciers.	1
11	**Award 1 mark** for: For holidays	1
12	**Award 1 mark** for both answers correct: ● It is a beautiful country. ● There are many things to see and do.	1
13	**Award 1 mark** for: myths and legends	1
14	**Award 1 mark** for: they did not like humans so might hurt them, or similar.	1
15	**Award 1 mark** for: The sun turned them into stone.	1
16	**Award 1 mark** for: terrible	1
17	**Award 1 mark** for both answers correct: ● gold ● silver	1
18	**Award 1 mark** for each of the following, up to a maximum of **2 marks**: ● the king's daughter ● huge amounts of land ● castles ● valuable prizes	2
19	**Award 1 mark** for: lightning frightens trolls away, or similar.	1

■SCHOLASTIC Guidance and mark schemes

Mark scheme for Test C: Paper 2

Q	Answers	Marks
1	**Award 1 mark** for any one of the following ideas, or similar: ● He is only four feet eleven inches tall, but he is a giant. ● He is a giant. ● Giants are not real.	1
2	**Award 1 mark** for next to the village	1
3	**Award 1 mark** for all three answers correct: the park, his house, his clothes	1
4	**Award 1 mark** for: To dry his eyes	1
5	**Award 1 mark** for both pairs of rhyming words matched correctly. cried – sighed groaned – moaned	1
6	**Award 1 mark** for: The people in the next village were complaining.	1
7	**Award 1 mark** for each plausible reason given, up to a maximum of **2 marks**, such as: ● He thought he was very important. ● He felt like an explorer. ● He didn't have enough time to think of a name, so he used his own.	2
8	**Award 1 mark** for: Everything	1
9	**Award 1 mark** for all three answers correct. RAAAH a lot, terrify their villagers, eat cows	1
10	**Award 1 mark** for: splashed	1
11	**Award 1 mark** for a tidal wave.	1
12	**Award 1 mark** for: Four feet eleven inches	1
13	**Award 1 mark** for any one of the following ideas: ● It is all right to be different and to not fit in. ● Sometimes what we want isn't what we really want.	1
14	**Award 1 mark** for any reasonable answer, such as: ● Oleg will return and be a proper giant. ● Oleg will solve his problems and fit in again. ● Oleg will never return.	1
15	**Award 1 mark** for inside Oscar's head / in his head	1
16	**Award 1 mark** for: alligator and elephant	1
17	**Award 1 mark** for any two of: mutter, squeak, squawk or jingle	1
18	**Award 1 mark** for all numbers correct. ① Oscar goes to sleep. ④ Oscar's Zoo disappears. ③ The animals have a feast. ② The Wallabear and Koalaby are in a tree.	1
19	**Award 1 mark** for any one of the following: the writer / the author / the poet / the person who wrote the poem / Graham Fletcher	1

SCHOLASTIC

National Curriculum
READING
TESTS

Test A

| Paper 1 | Paper 2 Reading booklet | Paper 2 Questions booklet |

✓ **Prepare with confidence for the new National Tests**
These are the most authentic practice papers for the new-format Key Stage 1 tests

✓ **All the support you need!**
Each test comes with a full mark scheme and clear guidance so you can check progress

✓ **Great value for money!**
In this pack you get three complete tests, plus detailed answers and guidance

Test B

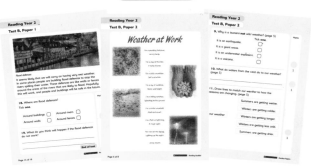

| Paper 1 | Paper 2 Reading booklet | Paper 2 Questions booklet |

Guidance and mark schemes

Test C

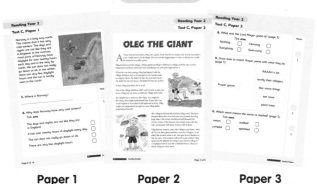

| Paper 1 | Paper 2 Reading booklet | Paper 3 Questions booklet |

Keep on track with other key Scholastic titles:

National Curriculum English Practice Book Year 2
ISBN 978-1407-12895-5

National Curriculum English Revision Guide Year 2
ISBN 978-1407-15914-0

National Curriculum Reading Tests for Year 2

£7.99

SCHOLASTIC

ISBN 978-1-407-15911-9

9 781407 159119

www.scholastic.co.uk